I Like
Colours

Barbara Jean Hicks and Lila Prap

HUTCHINSON
LONDON SYDNEY AUCKLAND JOHANNESBURG

Wacky

Colour

For Miguel
BJH

I LIKE COLOURS
A HUTCHINSON BOOK 0 09 189308 9
Published in Great Britain by Hutchinson,
an imprint of Random House Children's Books
This edition published 2005
1 3 5 7 9 10 8 6 4 2

RANDOM HOUSE CHILDREN'S BOOKS
61–63 Uxbridge Road, London W5 5SA
A division of The Random House Group Ltd

RANDOM HOUSE AUSTRALIA (PTY) LTD
20 Alfred Street, Milsons Point, Sydney,
New South Wales 2061, Australia

RANDOM HOUSE NEW ZEALAND LTD
18 Poland Road, Glenfield, Auckland 10, New Zealand

RANDOM HOUSE (PTY) LTD
Endulini, 5A Jubilee Road, Parktown 2193, South Africa

THE RANDOM HOUSE GROUP Limited Reg. No. 954009
www.kidsatrandomhouse.co.uk

A CIP catalogue record for this book is available from the British Library.

Printed in Singapore

quacky

quick

and slow

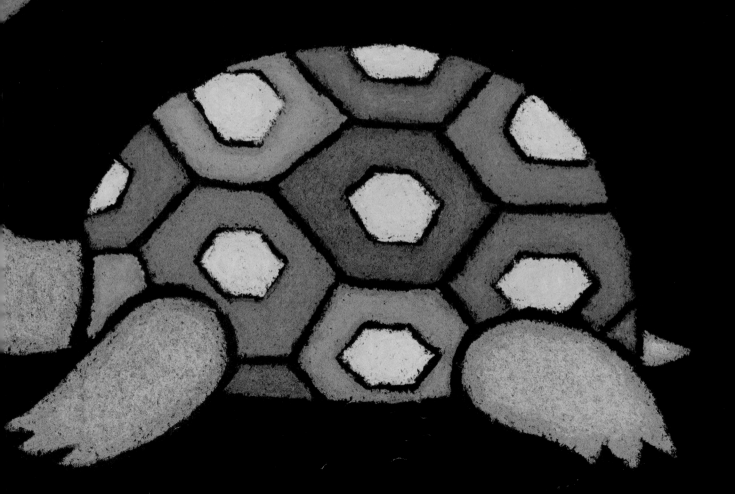

friendly

and low

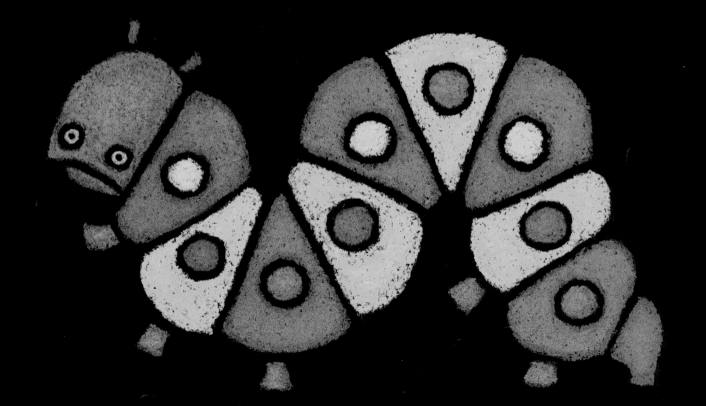

striped

and spotted

shallow

deep

quiet

loud

awake

asleep

tiny

tall

a lot

enough for me...

enough

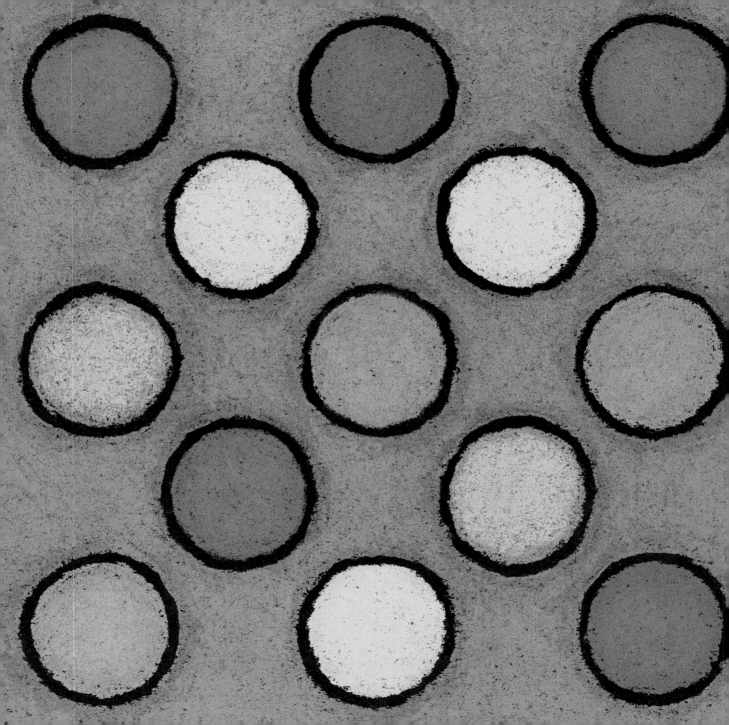